THIS BOOK BELONGS TO

_____

_____

_____

Ian Beck's
PICTURE
BOOK

Ian Beck's
PICTURE
BOOK

A first book of pictures
for very young children

For Lily

Scholastic Children's Books,
Commonwealth House, 1-19 New Oxford Street,
London WC1A 1NU, UK
a division of Scholastic Ltd
London ~ New York ~ Toronto ~ Sydney ~ Auckland

First published in hardback by Scholastic Ltd, 1994
This edition published by Scholastic Ltd, 1996

Copyright © Ian Beck, 1994

ISBN: 0 590 13715 8

Typeset by Graphiti Arts Ltd
Printed in Hong Kong by Paramount Printing Group

book

garden

ball

house

flowers

sheep

run

aeroplane

cat

swing

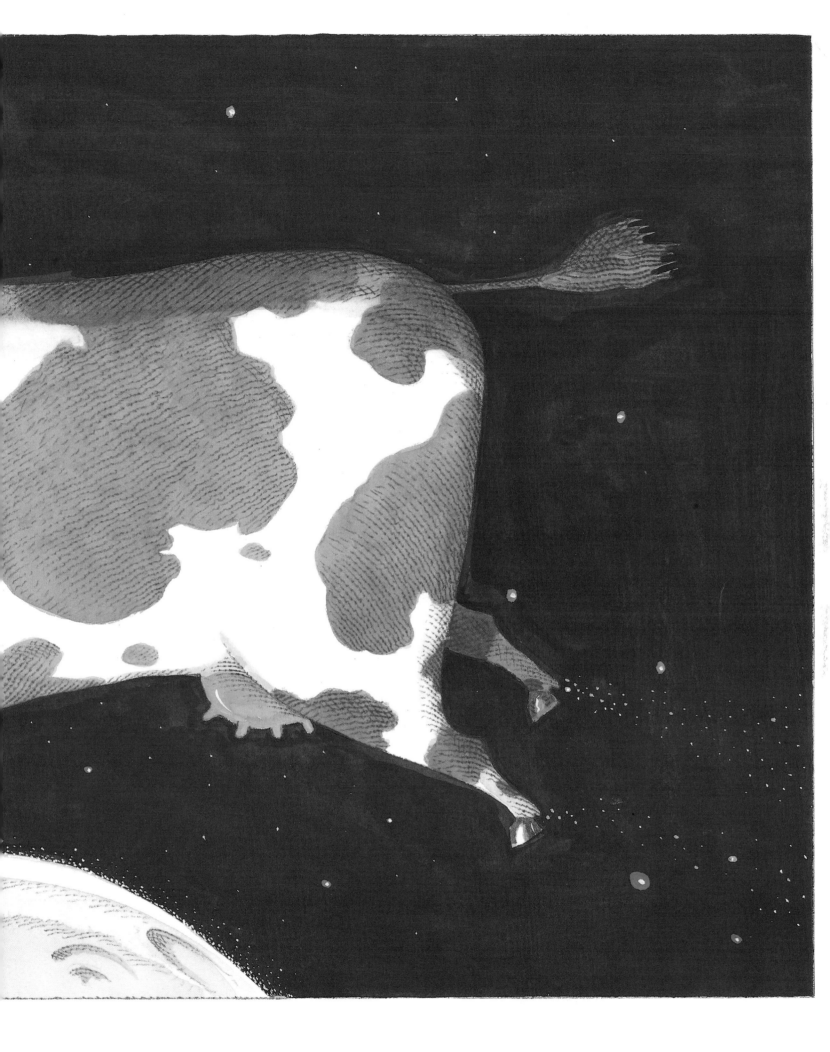

COW

snow

teddy

shadow

clouds

sea

face

jump

sun

wind

ship

stand still

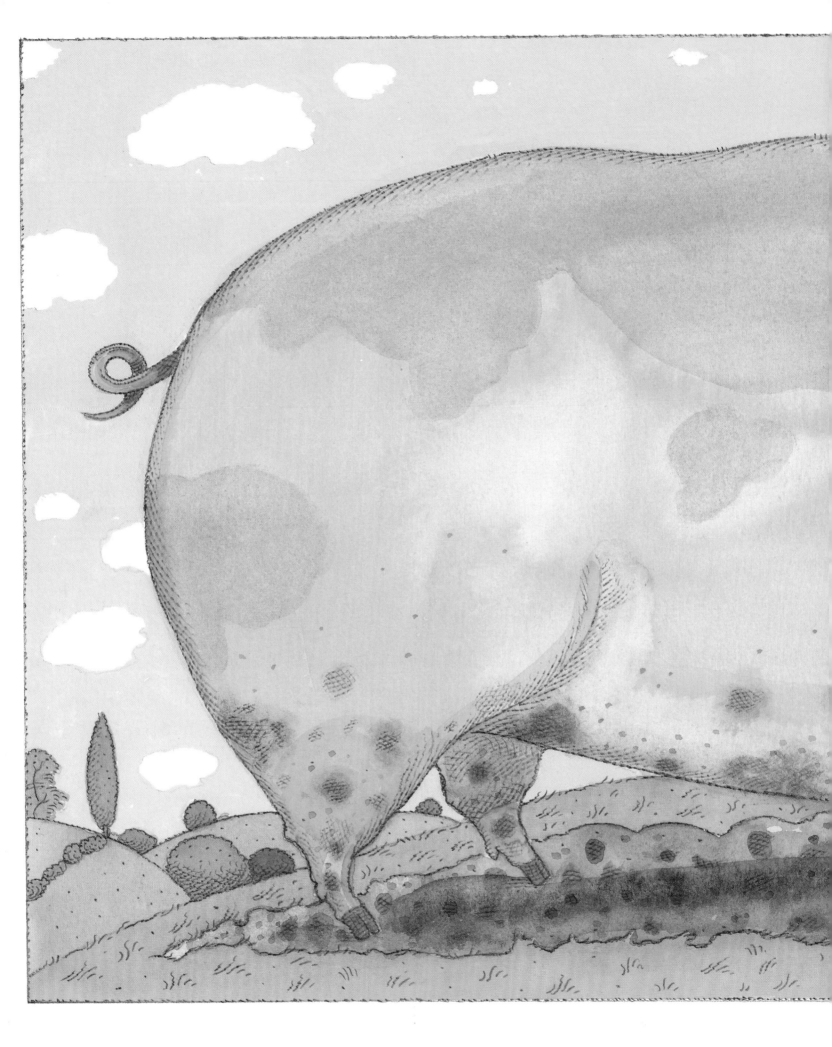

pig

balloon

duck

rain

moon

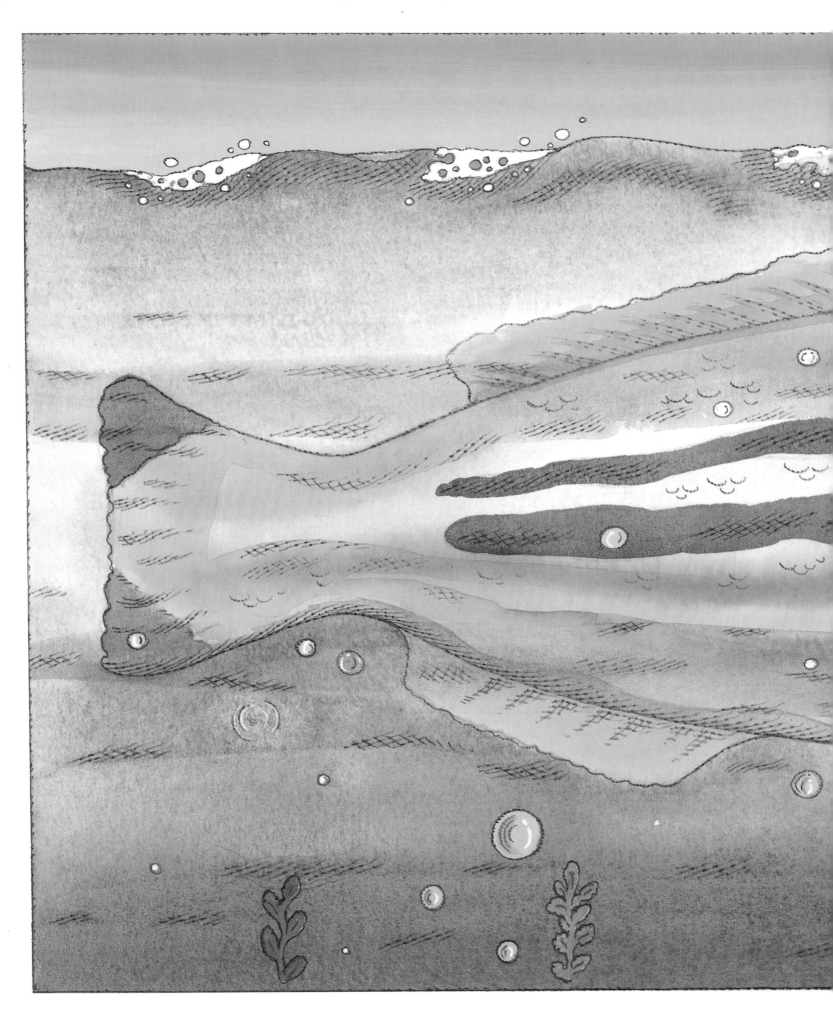

fish

dog

night

bed